C000277471

The Smallholder's D.I.Y

by
Michael Roberts

Edited by
Sara Roadnight

Photography &
Illustrations by
Michael Roberts

The Smallholder's D.I.Y
© 1999 Michael Roberts
Published by Gold Cockerel Books
ISBN 0 947870 17 2

Printed by Bartlett & Son Printers
Swan Yard, Okehampton Street, St Thomas, Exeter.
Tel. 01392 254086

Conditions of Sale

This book is sold subject to the condition that the designs and copyright are not for commercial reproduction without permission of the designer and copyright holder.

All rights reserved. No part of this publication may be reproduced, stored in a retrieval system or transmitted, in any form or by any means, electronic, mechanical or otherwise, without the prior written permission of the copyright owners and publishers.

WARNING

All the timber used in the construction of these items is standard rough sawn timber used mainly by the building trade. The biggest problem is the fact that it comes in a jumble of sizes, mainly metric or metric equivalents of imperial sizes, and some according to how the wood machinist felt that day! So do be careful in selecting your timber, and in some cases make allowances against my drawings and measurements. For instance 2" x 1" is often 4.5cm x 2cm, but in metric terms is 5cm x 2.5cm.

I have used treated wood (tanalised, but there are several trade names for pressure treated timber), and I always buy from the saw mill, not the builders' merchant, as the price difference is enormous. So shop around and don't use the large multiple stores. The small specialist saw mills in the country are very good value.

I do use screws rather than nails in most of my constructions, and nearly always prebore before putting them in. I used to be a 'nail-banger' but screws make a stronger construction. If you are buying screws, I would recommend Screwfix whose prices are very keen and whose service is excellent.

INTRODUCTION

Most people have looked at a product at a show or agricultural merchant, and then asked the price, recoiled and thought, I can make that myself. The two main problems involved with making an item at home are one, getting the design right first time, and two, finding the time to make it.

What I have offered here is a selection of products which I have made and used myself, so that I know they work. Everyone can make improvements to suit their particular circumstances or working methods, but as I say, all these items are tried and tested, and are very easy to put together.

We hope you will find them useful and enjoy making them.

MICHAEL D.L. ROBERTS & SARA ROADNIGHT

KENNERLEIGH 1999

SMALLHOLDERS D.I.Y.

CONTENTS

SHEEP HAY RACK

For years I had used a galvanised metal hay rack which I found very wasteful. Most of these racks allow too much hay to be pulled out by the sheep and don't collect the bits that drop down, so consequently there is an awful mess around the rack and this in turn kills the grass. The other irritating point is that, having struggled across a wet field with a bale of hay, you then have to put the bale on the ground (wet and muddy) to open the rack. So I came up with this design because a) I wanted a mobile hay rack that I could move daily by myself to minimise poaching the ground around it, and b) when I had struggled across the field with my heavy bale of hay I could put it on the roof of the hay rack, (which slides either way), so that I could cut the strings and fill up from either end, and c) I could have a hay rack which kept the waste to a minimum. The secret of this rack is the two pieces of weld mesh inside, which only allow the sheep to pull out a mouthful at a time, any extra dropping back into the box. It is quite heavy but this construction has to be strong because of rubbing and butting of horned sheep. The equivalent metal (wasteful) hay racks retail for about £150.00 but this one has cost less than £85.00. It copes with 15-20 sheep and the savings in hay are amazing.

Build up the base first and then add the ends. Make up the sides and fix them in position. Turn the whole thing over to fit the axle, wheels and feet blocks. Carefully turn it back onto the wheels and build in the boxes for the sliding handles which I have used to stop the sheep from knocking them about. Ensure the sliding handles are a sloppy or loose fit, because they will expand when they are damp or wet.

Now make up the roof. Again, make this a sloppy fit because there is nothing worse than a roof that doesn't slide when it is pouring with rain or snowing!

The roof will stick during frosts but if you jerk it up at one end that should sort it out. Don't forget to mastic the join along the top. I find also that a good coat of Cuprinol once a year helps to repel water.

Every now and then it is important to clean out the seeds and other debris which build up at the bottom of the box.

The wheels are available from most agricultural merchants.

1

SHEEP HAY RACK   FLOOR & ENDS.

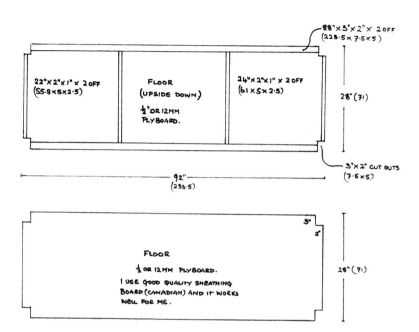

88"x3"x2" x 2 OFF
(223.5 x 7.5 x 5)

22"X2"X1" X 2 OFF
(55.8x5x2.5)

FLOOR
(UPSIDE DOWN)
½" OR 12MM
PLYBOARD.

24"X2"X1" X 2 OFF
(61 X 5 X 2.5)

28" (71)

92"
(233.5)

3"x2" CUT OUTS
(7.5 x 5)

3"

2"

FLOOR
½ OR 12MM PLYBOARD.
I USE GOOD QUALITY SHEATHING
BOARD (CANADIAN) AND IT WORKS
WELL FOR ME.

28" (71)

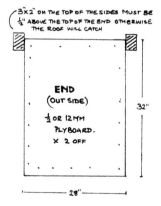

3"X2" ON THE TOP OF THE SIDES MUST BE
½" ABOVE THE TOP OF THE END OTHERWISE
THE ROOF WILL CATCH

END
(OUT SIDE)
½ OR 12MM
PLYBOARD.
X 2 OFF

32"

28"

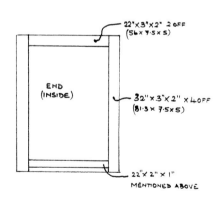

END
(INSIDE)

22"X3"X2" 2 OFF
(56 x 7.5 x 5)

32"X3"X2" X 4 OFF
(81.3 x 7.5 x 5)

22"X 2" X 1"
MENTIONED ABOVE

3

SHEEP HAY RACK SIDES.

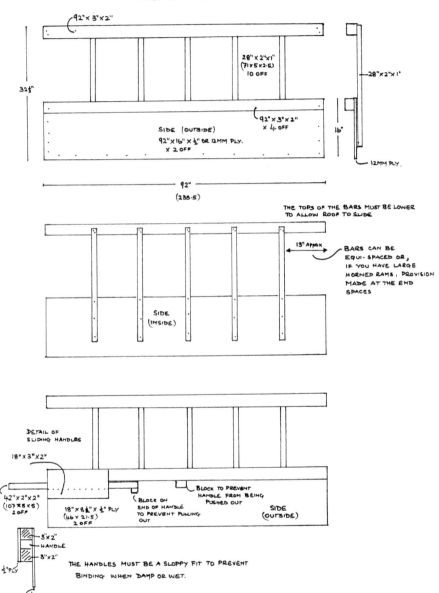

92" x 3" x 2"

28" x 2" x 1"
(71 x 5 x 2.5)
10 OFF

32½"

SIDE (OUTSIDE)
92" x 16" x ½" OR 12MM PLY.
X 2 OFF

92" x 3" x 2"
X 4 OFF

28" x 2" x 1"

16"

12MM PLY.

|← 92" →|
(233.5)

THE TOPS OF THE BARS MUST BE LOWER
TO ALLOW ROOF TO SLIDE.

13" Approx

BARS CAN BE
EQUI- SPACED OR,
IF YOU HAVE LARGE
HORNED RAMS, PROVISION
MADE AT THE END
SPACES

SIDE
(INSIDE)

DETAIL OF
SLIDING HANDLES

18" x 3" x 2"

42" x 2" x 2"
(107 x 5 x 5)
1 OFF

18" x 8½" x ½" PLY
(46 x 21.5)
2 OFF

BLOCK ON
END OF HANDLE
TO PREVENT PULLING
OUT

BLOCK TO PREVENT
HANDLE FROM BEING
PUSHED OUT

SIDE
(OUTSIDE)

3" x 2"
HANDLE
3" x 2"

½" PLY

½" PLY

THE HANDLES MUST BE A SLOPPY FIT TO PREVENT
BINDING WHEN DAMP OR WET.

4

SHEEP HAY RACK   UNDERGEAR & ROOF.

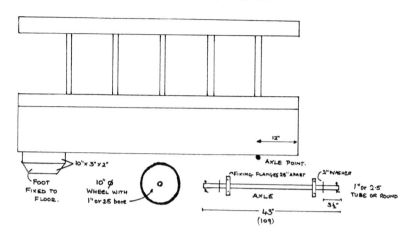

12"

● AXLE POINT.

10" x 3" x 2"

FOOT
FIXED TO
FLOOR.

10" ⌀
WHEEL WITH
1" or 2.5 bore

Fixing FLANGES 28" APART

2" WASHER

AXLE

1" or 2.5
TUBE OR ROUND

3½"

43"
(109)

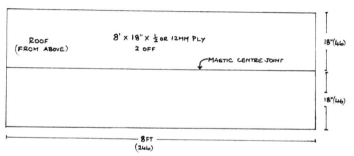

ROOF
(FROM ABOVE)

8' x 18" x ½ 12MM PLY
2 OFF

MASTIC CENTRE JOINT

18"(46)

18"(46)

8FT
(244)

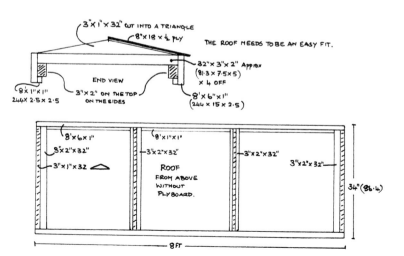

3" x 1" x 32" CUT INTO A TRIANGLE
8" x 18 x ½ PLY

THE ROOF NEEDS TO BE AN EASY FIT.

32" x 3" x 2" Approx
(81.3 x 7.5 x 5)
x 4 OFF

END VIEW

8" x 1" x 1"
244 x 2.5 x 2.5

3" x 2" ON THE TOP
ON THE SIDES

8" x 6" x 1"
(244 x 15 x 2.5)

8' x 6 x 1"

8' x 2" x 32"

3" x 1" x 32

8' x 1" x 1"

3½" x 2" x 32"

ROOF
FROM ABOVE
WITHOUT
PLYBOARD.

3" x 2" x 32"

3" x 2" x 32"

34"(86.4)

8FT

5

SHEEP MINERAL BLOCK HOLDER

I have used this mineral block holder for years, and have found it to be very successful. First it keeps the block clean, and secondly, you can move the holder around the field to avoid any area becoming poached. The mineral block fits in tightly so it does not get tipped out.

Cut the 3" x 2" to length and nail the 6" x 1" boarding to it with 2 1/2" galvanised nails. Cut out the 2" x 1" and nail it onto the plinth or boarding. It is best to have a new block handy to make sure of a tight fit. Nail or screw from both sides and underneath to ensure the block is steady.

6

MINERAL BLOCK HOLDER.

6"x1"x13" (52 x 2·6 x 33) 2 OFF

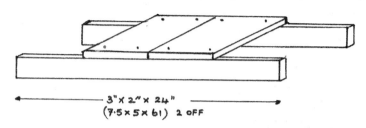

3" x 2" x 24"
(7·5 x 5 x 61) 2 OFF

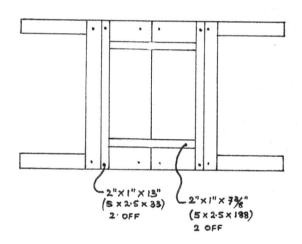

2"x1"x13"
(5 x 2·5 x 33)
2 OFF

2"x1"x7¾"
(5 x 2·5 x 188)
2 OFF

TRADITIONAL SHEEP TROUGH

You can make this trough as long or short as you want; I always make them 12ft or 10ft long. Once you have made a template for the feet, these troughs can be put together very quickly.

Cut the long timbers to size, and then cut two lengths 20" long of 6" x 1". Cut out the diagonals, and fix the feet equidistant from the ends. If the trough is 12ft long, the feet need to be 3 1/2ft from each end.

Nail the sides into the valleys of the feet, making sure that they are of equal height. Carefully nail in the triangular end pieces without splitting the wood.

It is important to band up the feet and the ends to stop splitting or damage to the trough. This can be done with soft fencing wire and light staples (3/4"). Make a loop at each end of the wire to stop it from slipping out. Alternatively you can use builders' banding which is very satisfactory.

These troughs normally last about 10-15 years, and are best stored upside down. I always use tanalised wood.

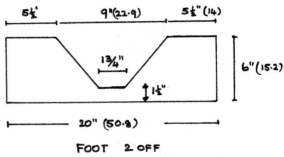

FOOT   2 OFF
MADE FROM 6"×1"

SIDES

2 OFF

12' or NEAREST
 6" × 1"
(3600⁺ × 15·2 × 2·5)

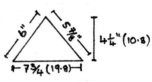

END
2 OFF
MADE FROM 6"×1"

10

LIVESTOCK TROUGH

Before you start you require a bench saw with a swinging or adjustable table, as you need to be able to cut the chamfers on the 6" x 1".

This trough can be used for a variety of livestock, sheep, goats, calves and young horses, as it is sturdy and has an anti-spill strip along the top edge. The bars across the top of the trough make it easy to handle.

Cut the 6" x 1" into lengths of 8", and set your saw up to chamfer the one edge on the side pieces and both edges on the floor piece.

Cut out the foot pieces and build up the trough, also nailing the floor to the side pieces all the way long. Add in the end pieces and end feet.

Nail in the anti-spill strip. You may need to nick a piece out of this strip under the cross bars.

Once you have fixed the trough together, it is important to band up the ends and the central feet with either soft plain fencing wire, or builders' banding. This will hold it together when it is undergoing rough treatment.

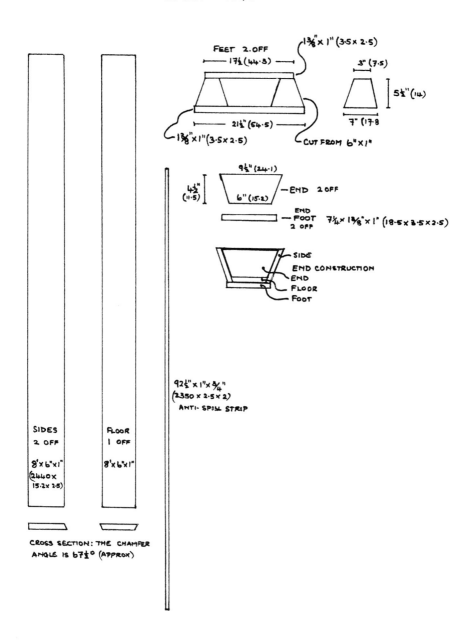

FEET 2.OFF

17½" (44.3)

1⅜" x 1" (3.5 x 2.5)

3" (7.5)

5¼" (14)

7" (17.8)

21½" (54.5)

1⅜" x 1" (3.5 x 2.5)

CUT FROM 6" x 1"

9½" (24.1)

4½" (11.5)

6" (15.2)

— END 2 OFF

END FOOT 2 OFF

7¾ x 1⅜" x 1" (18.5 x 3.5 x 2.5)

SIDE

END CONSTRUCTION

END

FLOOR

FOOT

92½" x 1" x ¾" (2350 x 2.5 x 2)

ANTI- SPILL STRIP

SIDES
2 OFF

8' x 6" x 1"
(2440 x
15.2 x 2.5)

FLOOR
1 OFF

8' x 6" x 1"

CROSS SECTION: THE CHAMFER
ANGLE IS 67½° (APPROX)

13

SHEEP CRADLE

I wanted something to help me trim my sheeps' feet and enable me to dag them without too much bending. I had noticed in an old photograph that sheep used to be shorn on a bench, so I came up with this idea. Although not perfect, it does save the poor back! It is important to have a table or shelf nearby to hold all the necessary kit for clipping, marking, spraying, etc, and with certain sheep you will need another person to hold the legs still, but the system works well.

Walk or drag the sheep to stand beside the cradle, and roll her on. Once she is lying upside down on it sit on her sternum (breast bone), and start clipping her feet. You will need someone else's help for the dagging.

I am sure someone will improve on this simple design but the alternative metal contraptions are very expensive.

Cut up the wood for the legs and build up the sides with the handles. Then cut the cross members and screw these together and to the sides. Cut the 2" x 1" battens to length, and fasten them to the frame. Sandpaper all round.

SHEEP CRADLE.

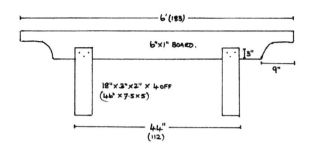

6' (183)

6"×1" BOARD.

3"

9"

18"×3"×2" × 4 OFF
(46" × 7.5 × 5)

44"
(112)

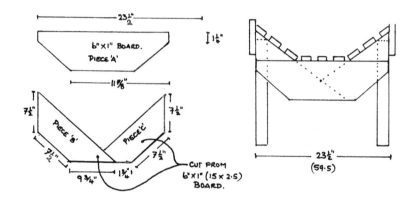

23½"

6" × 1" BOARD.
PIECE 'A'

1¼"

11⅝"

7½"   7½"

PIECE 'B'   PIECE 'C'

7½"   7½"

9¾"   1¾"

CUT FROM
6"×1" (15 × 2.5)
BOARD.

23½"
(59.5)

VIEW FROM ON TOP

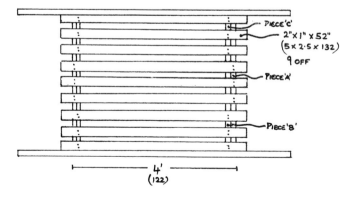

PIECE 'C'

2"×1" × 52"
(5 × 2.5 × 132)

9 OFF

PIECE 'A'

PIECE 'B'

4'
(122)

15

6FT SHEEP HURDLE

These hurdles are very quick and easy to put together and even more so if you have a jig to make them up on.

Cut the wood to the right lengths, position and nail into place with 1 1/2" panel pins. This enables you to handle the hurdle carefully without it falling to pieces, prior to bolting up. Turn over to the 'A' side and drill the hurdle to take 2" M6 bolts, then drill out the holes again to a depth of 3/8" or 1 cm to take the M6 pronged nut. Tap on the nuts and bolt up tightly from side 'B'.

Now fit the diagonals. Cut and make a tight fit - it is the diagonals that hold the hurdle in shape. Panel pin into place, double drill and bolt together.

I find that electric wire cut in lengths of 18" to 20" long makes excellent ties for holding these hurdles together.

Always ensure that good knot free timber is used; select it carefully when you buy.

6ft SHEEP HURDLE.

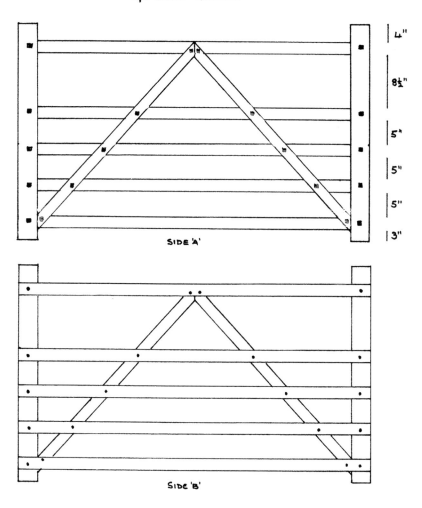

SIDE 'A'

4"

8½"

5"

5"

5"

3"

SIDE 'B'

POSTS   3"x1"x 40"   2 OFF
          (7.5 x 2.5 x 1015)

RAILS   2"x1"x 6'   5 OFF
          (5 x 2.5 x 1830)

DIAGONALS   2"x1"x 47" APPROX
             (5 x 2.5 x 1194)

ANGLE OF DIAGONAL 47½° both ends.

20 x 2" (50) M6 BOLTS %w PRONGED NUTS.

17

6FT HEAVY SHEEP OR PIG HURDLE

This is the heavier version of the 6ft sheep hurdle, a very robust item that will take some bashing about from pigs or rams. Cut the timber into correct lengths and position on a flat floor or work table. Use 1 1/2" panel pins to hold in place. Turn over so that side 'A' is facing up, and add in the diagonals. Make sure they are a tight fit as these hold the hurdles in shape. Panel pin in the diagonals and then drill holes to take 2" M6 bolts. Counter drill again to take the pronged nut to a depth of 3/8" or 1 cm, and tap on the pronged nuts. Turn the hurdle over again and bolt it up.

Select the timber you use with care, as a faulty rail looks bad and is a weak point.

Plain soft fencing wire ties these hurdles together.

18

6 FT HEAVY SHEEP OR PIG HURDLE.

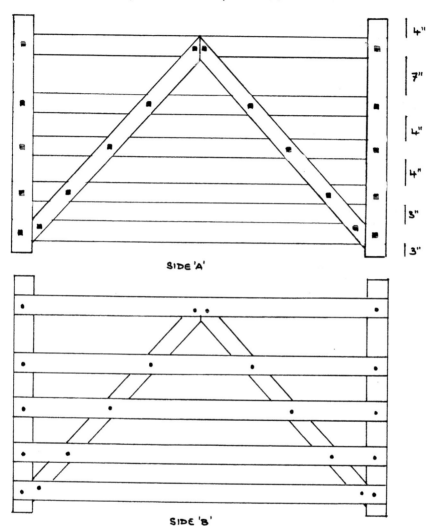

SIDE 'A'

4"
7"
4"
4"
3"
3"

SIDE 'B'

POSTS   3" x 1" x 40"   2 OFF
        (7·5 x 2·5 x 1015)

RAILS   3" x 1" x 6'   5 OFF
        (7·5 x 2·5 x 1830)

DIAGONALS   3" x 1" x 47" APPROX
            (7·5 x 2·6 x 1194)

ANGLE OF DIAGONAL 47½° BOTH ENDS

20 x 2" M6 BOLTS (50) ⁵/w PRONGED NUTS.

19

FODDER BOX FOR HANGING ON A HURDLE

You can use these boxes when lambing or showing; they keep the food dry and off the floor, and are simple to make.

Cut the timber to length, and nail or screw the floor to the back and the front boards. Put in the sides so that they are a tight fit, and fix to the floor, front and back boards. I have used some builder's strip to tie in the ends, but plain soft fencing wire will also work.

Cut the 1 1/8" flat to length, and mark with felt tip pen where the bends are to be. You can do this cold but it is easier to heat up the section to be bent with a gas torch. It is sometimes difficult to make an exact pair, so allowances should be made when bolting the hooked flat onto the box, in order to ensure that it hangs straight. If you use it for showing, write your name on the box, as these items have a habit of disappearing

FODDER BOX.

FLOOR
20" x 7⅝" x ½" PLY.
(50·8 x 20 x 12MM)

BACK.
20" x 6" x 1"
(50·8 x 15 x 2·5)

FRONT
20" x 5" x 1"
(50·8 x 12·5 x 2·5)

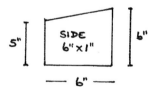

SIDE
6" x 1"

5"

6"

6"

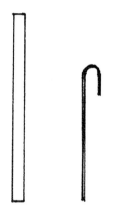

1⅛" (3) FLAT. (2MM) x
18" (46) LONG.
2 OFF

21

FORESTRY GATE

This idea came from forestry people who wanted a gate or frame to put across a vehicle access that wasn't used very often. I adapted this idea and put pig wire on instead of rabbit wire. This gate is placed in areas where access is sometimes required and it does make a very effective and cheap barrier. There is an area of one of my fields which is not easy to make hay out of, and I have turned it into a shelter belt and sheep handling corner, with the entrance closed by one of these gates.

Normally this frame drops onto two wooden hooks and behind two wooden pegs on the ground, but I just wire it to the posts with soft plain fencing wire. I have found that resting the frame on two house bricks sideways up, helps to keep the bottom rail off the ground and stops it from rotting too quickly.

I don't think there is any need for instructions about putting this together.

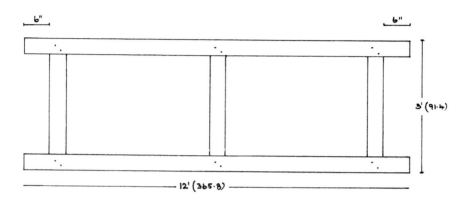

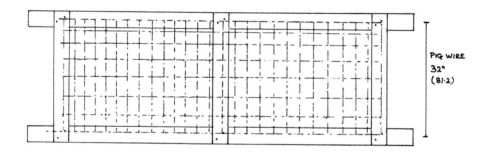

TIMBER : $3\frac{1}{2}$" X $1\frac{1}{2}$" (9×4) RAILS

HUNTING OR FOOTPATH GATE

These gates were made for those mounted members of the hunt who did not like to jump. They work equally well as footpath gates.

Most people don't have a morticing machine, so this construction is the next best thing.

There are three main criteria for making gates this way. First, choose your timber with care, making sure that it is of a regular size and thickness, and not bowed or warped. Second, the joints have to fit tightly between the spacers, so this calls for accurate and straight cuts of timber, and third, use lots of external wood glue.

Cut out the 4 lengths for the posts and the 3" x 1" for the 4 cross rails. Cut the top rail 3" x 2" to length and cut out the joints. Now start cutting out the spacers and commencing the sandwich construction. Use plenty of glue as you fit in the rails, and hold them in position with oval nails. Once all the rails are in place with spacers fitting tightly between, glue the outside posts to the assembly. Hold in position with small oval nails. Bore through the posts at the point where the rails meet, and tighten up the assembled gate, using 50mm galvanised roofing bolts and pronged nuts. Now add the diagonal rail, making a tight fit either end. This will stop the gate from going out of square.

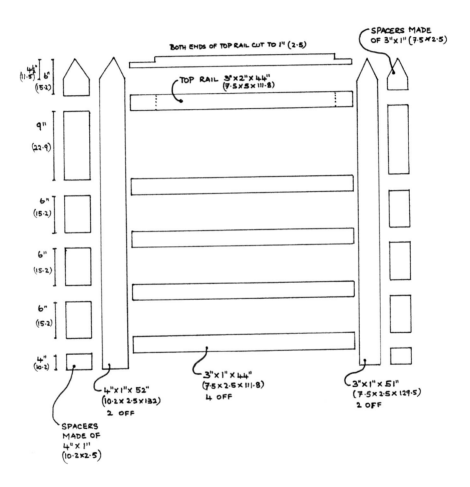

HUNTING OR FOOTPATH GATE.

BOTH ENDS OF TOP RAIL CUT TO 1" (2·5)

SPACERS MADE
OF 3"×1" (7·5×2·5)

TOP RAIL 3"×2"×44"
(7·5×5×111·8)

4½"
(11·5)   6"
(15·2)

9"
(22·9)

6"
(15·2)

6"
(15·2)

6"
(15·2)

4"
(10·2)

4"×1"× 52"
(10·2×2·5×132)
2 OFF

SPACERS
MADE OF
4"× 1"
(10·2×2·5)

3"×1"×44"
(7·5×2·5×111·8)
4 OFF

3"×1"× 51"
(7·5×2·5×129·5)
2 OFF

26

HUNTING OR FOOTPATH GATE

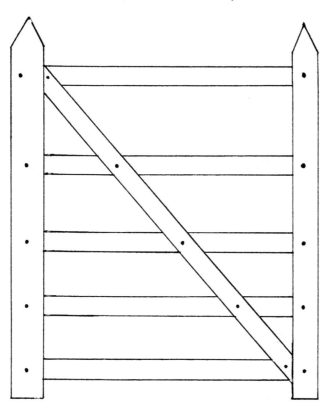

DIAGONAL. 3"x 1" x 57" Approx.
(7·5x 2·5x 145).

BOLT WITH PRONGED NUT

27

10' WOODEN GATE

There are occasions when you require a 9'6" gate or an odd size or you want to make your own to save money. If you haven't a morticing tool, and your carpentry skills are limited, this method of construction works well. I made such a gate 15 years ago and it is still going strong. The important points to remember when making gates are a) have a bold top rail, and b) brace the gate so that it will not move when it is hung except in the directions you want it to! This is why it is important to have tight square fitting joints and lots of glue, and also to ensure the timber is free of large knots and is the same size throughout.

Cut out the post pieces first, and then the cross rails. Next, cut the joints out of the top rail and start to assemble the gate. Cut out the spacers, glue and nail to the post on the floor, making sure the joints are as tight as possible. Glue the top side of the post assembly and now fix the other post board. Use oval nails to hold in place, prior to putting on the bolts and pronged nuts. You will need to counter drill the holes for the pronged nuts in order to get them to fit properly. The gate will be a bit floppy at this stage, but now add in the diagonals. You will need to chisel out the wedge pieces, or these can be precut out of the post boards to fit the diagonal rails. Put the diagonal rails in place, again with a tight fit, and nail to hold them in place while bolting up. (Use a few oval nails to do this). Drill and put a screw in the wedge cuts. Now pick up your gate. It should feel very solid and not at all bendy.

Gate irons or hinges are available at most agricultural merchants. Bolt these on, the long one on the top and the short one on the bottom. The long one must stretch along and incorporate the top rail, the bottom hinge can be moveable, so that if you are making a new gate for an old gate post, the gate can be made to fit. Creosote for extra life.

I have incorporated a step onto this gate so people can climb over it easily. This just slides on and can be screwed down.

10' WOODEN GATE

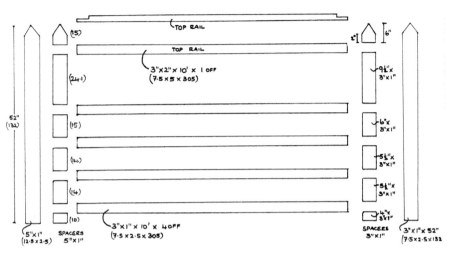

TOP RAIL

TOP RAIL

3"x2" x 10' x 1 OFF
(7.5 x 5 x 305)

52"
(132)

(15)

(24.1)

(15)

(14)

(14)

(10)

9½"x
3"x1"

6"x
3"x1"

5½"x
3"x1"

5½"x
3"x1"

4"x
3x1"

5"x1"
(12.5 x 2.5)

SPACERS
5"x1"

3"x1" x 10' x 4 OFF
(7.5 x 2.5 x 305)

SPACERS
3"x1"

3"x1"x 52"
(7.5 x 2.5 x 132)

2"[6"

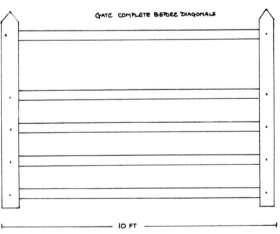

GATE COMPLETE BEFORE DIAGONALS

|— 10 FT —|

30

10' WOODEN GATE.

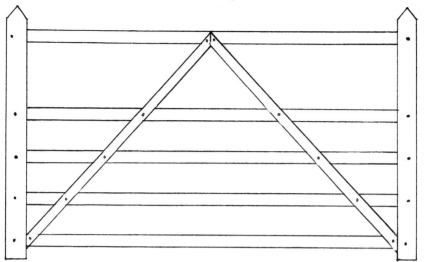

DIAGONAL RAIL 70" (178) APPROX. 2 OFF

MAKE DIAGONALS A TIGHT FIT.

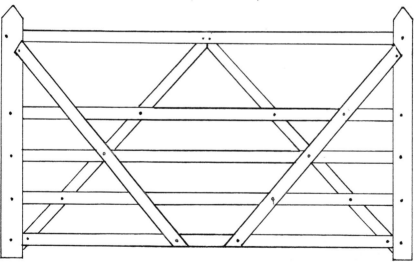

DIAGONAL RAIL 68" (173) APPROX).

IF MAKING A GATE TO FIT AN ODD SIZED OPENING
TRY TO MAKE THE DIAGONAL MEET AT THE SAME
PLACE FOR EXTRA STRENGTH.

31

BROODER

This is a multi-purpose brooder, as you can use it for goslings, ducklings, chicks, guineafowl chicks, quail chicks, etc.

The box is made up of 3/8" or 9mm plyboard and held together with smooth pieces of 1" x 1". The smoothness is important when you are cleaning it so that the cloth or sponge doesn't snag all the time.

Cut out the plyboard, and make up the floor first. Add on the sides and then the front and back. Drill and screw in the corner posts. Drill and screw the sides to take the front cover.

Make up the brooder top and staple on the plastic gauze. This is green and can be bought from most good garden centres. You can use 1/2" wire netting, but I find the green gauze reduces bright light and helps to stop feather pecking.

Cut out the plyboard for the two tops over the brooder heater. These help to keep the heat in as well as the chicks, and can be moved around to accommodate the heater lamp.

The heater is a standard ceramic bulb with an 11" aluminium shade.

32

BROODER.

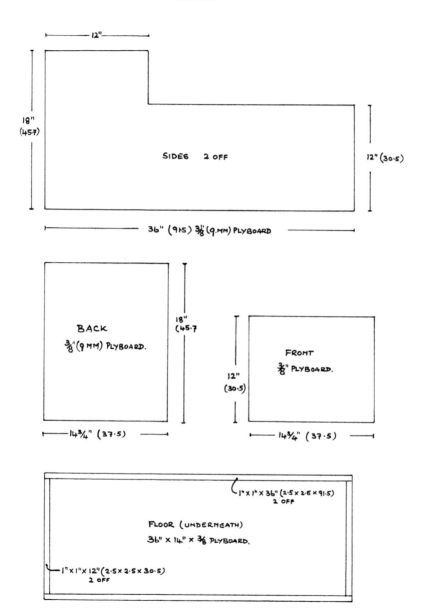

SIDES   2 OFF

18"
(45·7)

12"

12" (30·5)

36" (915) 3/8" (9.mm) PLYBOARD

BACK
3/8" (9 mm) PLYBOARD.

18"
(45·7

14¾" (37·5)

FRONT
3/8" PLYBOARD.

12"
(30·5)

14¾" (37·5)

1" × 1" × 36" (2·5 × 2·5 × 91·5)
2 OFF

FLOOR (UNDERNEATH)
36" × 14" × 3/8" PLYBOARD.

1" × 1" × 12" (2·5 × 2·5 × 30·5)
2 OFF

33

BROODER.

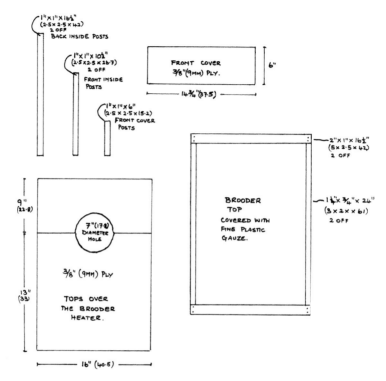

1"×1"×16½"
(2.5×2.5×42)
2 OFF
BACK INSIDE POSTS

1"×1"×10½"
(2.5×2.5×26.7)
2 OFF
FRONT INSIDE POSTS

1"×1¼"×6"
(2.5×2.5×15.2)
FRONT COVER POSTS

FRONT COVER
⅜"(9MM) PLY.

6"

14¾"(37.5)

2"×1"×16½"
(5×2.5×42)
2 OFF

BROODER
TOP
COVERED WITH
FINE PLASTIC
GAUZE.

1¼"×¾"×24"
(3×2×61)
2 OFF

9"
(22.8)

7"(17.8)
DIAMETER
HOLE

⅜" (9MM) PLY

13"
(33)

TOPS OVER
THE BROODER
HEATER.

16" (40.5)

34

OUTDOOR BROODER

I have given you a design for an indoor brooder, and here is an outdoor one. Many years ago, I saw such a brooder with a paraffin heater. That was a complicated affair, but I am very pleased with this one. It has an indoor and an outdoor section, the indoors can be heated with a lamp, and the floors are all interchangeable. There is a solid removable floor/tray for indoors, and a half-inch weld mesh floor in the outdoor area which is interchangeable with the indoor one, and a 1" x 1" wire mesh frame for the roof of the outdoor area. Again this will fit the floor of the indoor and outdoor areas if need be. It can also have plastic sheeting stapled to it, to make a weatherproof outdoor area. This brooder can be used at any time of year, which is useful for raising early pullets or show birds. The apex roof slides over the outdoor area for cleaning purposes and it has a door built into it as well for feeding and inspection. Two sizes of pop hole are incorporated for weather conditions and size of birds, and there is also an outside pop hole so that an 8ft run, as described in Poultry House Construction, can be added. The whole brooder is easy to clean and service and is entirely rat proof; I only have to check my birds twice a day with this system.

Make up the sides first, and then the end and middle panels. Don't forget the pop hole on the outdoor section. Cut up the batten for the floor panels, and drill and nail, (if you don't drill, you will finish up with split ends). Staple the wire mesh panels onto the frames, and nail the plyboard onto its frame. Cut the two lengths of board, one for the ramp, the other for the space on the top of the outdoor area. Assemble all these parts. The brooder now feels quite firm and solid. Next construct the roof. Make the sliding area fairly sloppy or loose fitting, as when the wood gets damp it will expand and make the roof difficult to slide forward. Add a cup hook inside the roof area for the electric lamp. Make sure that the plug and socket for the lamp are under cover in the roof or wrapped in waterproof plastic. Paint with Cuprinol.

OUTDOOR BROODER (SIDES AND ENDS)

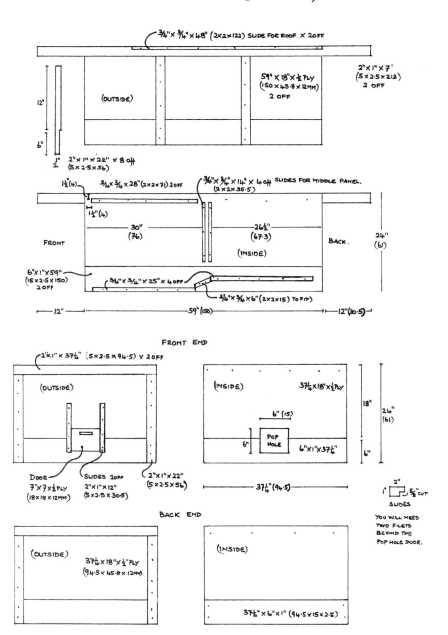

37

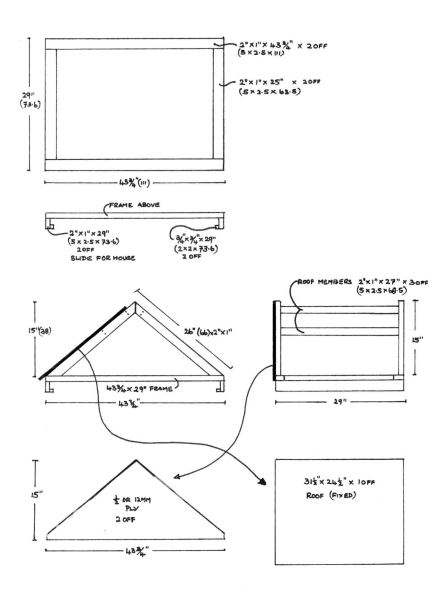

29"
(73.6)

2"×1"× 43¾" × 2 OFF
(5 × 2.5 × 111)

2"×1"× 25" × 2 OFF
(5 × 2.5 × 63.5)

43¾" (111)

FRAME ABOVE

2"×1"× 29"
(5 × 2.5 × 73.6)
2 OFF
SLIDE FOR HOUSE

3¾"× ¾"× 29"
(2 × 2 × 73.6)
2 OFF

ROOF MEMBERS 2"×1"× 27" × 3 OFF
(5 × 2.5 × 68.5)

15"(38)

26" (66) × 2"×1"

43¾"× 29" FRAME

43¾"

15"

29"

15"

½ OR 12MM
PLY
2 OFF

43¾"

31½"× 24½" × 1 OFF
ROOF (FIXED)

38

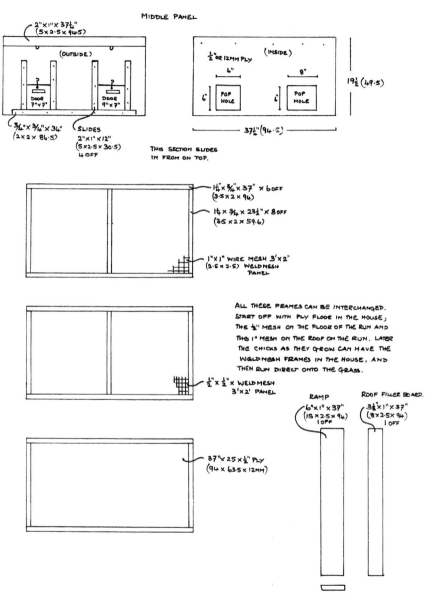

OUTDOOR BROODER (MIDDLE PANEL & FLOORS.)

MIDDLE PANEL

2"×1"×37½"
(5×2·5×94·5)

(OUTSIDE)

DOOR 7"×7"   DOOR 9"×7"

3¼"×3¼"×34"
(2×2×86·5)

SLIDES
2"×1"×12"
(5×2·5×30·5)
4 OFF

THIS SECTION SLIDES
IN FROM ON TOP.

½" OR 12MM PLY   (INSIDE)

6"   8"

6"   POP HOLE   6"   POP HOLE

19½ (49·5)

37½" (94·5)

1¼"×¾"×37" × 6 OFF
(3·5×2×94)

1¼×¾ × 23½" × 8 OFF
(3·5×2×59·6)

1"×1" WIRE MESH 3'×2'
(2·5×2·5) WELD MESH
PANEL

ALL THESE FRAMES CAN BE INTERCHANGED.
START OFF WITH PLY FLOOR IN THE HOUSE;
THE ½" MESH ON THE FLOOR OF THE RUN AND
THE 1" MESH ON THE ROOF ON THE RUN. LATER
THE CHICKS AS THEY GROW CAN HAVE THE
WELDMESH FRAMES IN THE HOUSE, AND
THEN RUN DIRECT ONTO THE GRASS.

½" × ½" × WELDMESH
3'×2' PANEL

RAMP
6"×1"×37"
(15×2·5×94)
1 OFF

ROOF FILLER BOARD.
3½"×1"×37"
(8×2·5×94)
1 OFF

37"×25×½" PLY
(94 × 63·5 × 12MM)

THE RAMP NEEDS TO BE SLIGHTLY
CHAMFERED ON THE HOUSE SIDE
SO THAT THE FRAME OR FLOOR
FITS IN.

39

OUTDOOR BROODER (ROOF)

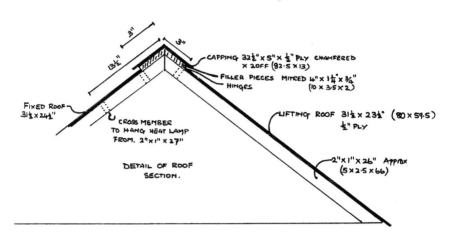

CAPPING 32½" X 5" X ½" PLY CHAMFERED X 2OFF (82.5 X 13)

FILLER PIECES MITRED 4" X 1¼" X ¾" (10 X 3.5 X 2)

HINGES

FIXED ROOF 31½ X 24½"

LIFTING ROOF 31½ X 23½" (80 X 59.5) ½" PLY

CROSS MEMBER TO HANG HEAT LAMP FROM. 2" X 1" X 27"

DETAIL OF ROOF SECTION.

2" X 1" X 26" Approx (5 X 2.5 X 66)

LIFTING ROOF

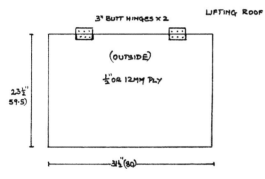

3" BUTT HINGES X 2

(OUTSIDE)

½" OR 12MM PLY

23½" 59.5)

31½" (80)

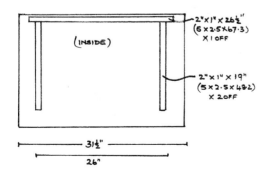

(INSIDE)

2" X 1" X 26½" (5 X 2.5 X 67.3) X 1 OFF

2" X 1" X 19" (5 X 2.5 X 48.2) X 2OFF

31½"

26"

40

HEN DUST BATH

Make up the frame for the base. Nail 2" x 1" to 3" x 2" and then nail 1/2" plyboard floor to frame. Fix sides 3ft x 8" to frame with strip on the inside. Now fix end panels to frame, and carefully fix corner posts. Drill and screw these into place. Add on the top rail slightly above the corner posts and again drill and screw. Turn it upside down and fix the feet. Screw these on with 4" screws and 2 1/2" screws into the diagonal. File the ends of the axle so the wheels slip over easily, and drill it to be able to put split pins and washers in to hold the wheels in the correct position. Paint, and fix to the frame with 2 1/2" nails.

Cut 2" x 1" and 1 1/2" x 3/4" laths and nail together. Cut out triangular pieces and fix to the 2" x 1" laths. Drill and screw. Cut out roof panels 40" x 20" and fix one side with 1 1/4" size 6 screws. Cut 2" x 1" lath for the roof; this helps to stop it warping. Saw off the diagonal 125 degrees or 55 degrees (approx) to fit snugly under the roof joint. Glue along the length and screw into place. Now fix on the other roof panel and screw it into place. Sandpaper down and slide the roof onto the top rail/handles. If it all fits well take the roof off again and paint it with Cuprinol or wood preservative.

DUST BATH FOR HENS.

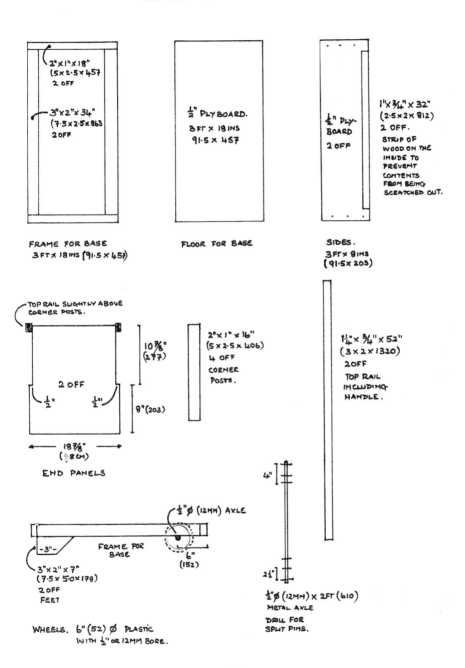

2"×1"×18"
(5×2·5×457)
2 OFF

3"×2"×34"
(7·5×2·5×863)
2 OFF

FRAME FOR BASE
3 FT × 18 INS (91·5 × 457)

½" PLYBOARD.
3 FT × 18 INS
91·5 × 457

FLOOR FOR BASE

¼" PLY-
BOARD
2 OFF

1"× ¾" × 32"
(2·5×2× 812)
2 OFF.
STRIP OF
WOOD ON THE
INSIDE TO
PREVENT
CONTENTS
FROM BEING
SCRATCHED OUT.

SIDES.
3 FT × 8 INS
(91·5 × 203)

TOP RAIL SLIGHTLY ABOVE
CORNER POSTS.

2 OFF

½"   ½"

10⅞"
(277)

8"(203)

18⅞"
(48 CM)

END PANELS

2"×1"×16"
(5×2·5×406)
4 OFF
CORNER
POSTS.

1¼"× ¾"×52"
(3×2×1320)
2 OFF
TOP RAIL
INCLUDING
HANDLE.

FRAME FOR
BASE

-3"-

3"×2"×7"
(7·5×5·0×178)
2 OFF
FEET

½"⌀ (12MM) AXLE

6"
(152)

WHEELS. 6"(52) ⌀ PLASTIC
WITH ½" OR 12MM BORE.

4"

2¼"

½"⌀ (12MM) × 2FT (610)
METAL AXLE
DRILL FOR
SPLIT PINS.

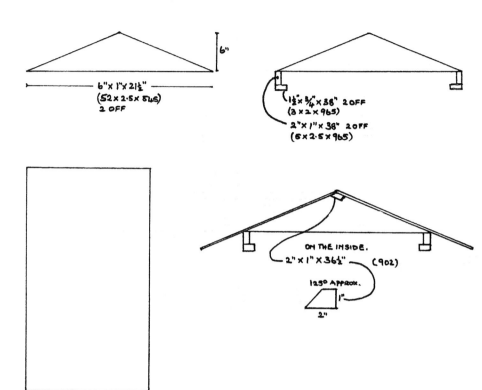

6"x 1"x 21½"
(52 x 2.5 x 545)
2 OFF

1½ x ¾" x 38" 2OFF
(3 x 2 x 965)

2"x 1"x 38" 2OFF
(5 x 2.5 x 965)

ON THE INSIDE.

2" x 1" X 36½"   (902)

125° APPROX.

1"

2"

ROOF PANELS

½"(12MM) PLYBOARD
20" x 40"(508 x 1016)
2 OFF

FREE STANDING NEST BOX

This nest box can be used indoors or outdoors. If you have a large shed or barn under deep litter, this form of nest box is ideal and very easy to keep clean. It can also be used out on the range, as some hens love to lay away from the main house if they can, and this nest box will attract these birds.

Cut the plyboard for the ends, and jigsaw out the pop holes. Nail or screw on the legs, and add the floor batten. Fit in the floor and then attach the sides. Add in the entrance baffles. Screw in the 2" x 1" on the roof apex, and the batten on the top of the sides. Fix the roof on next, and screw on the hinges. Add on the outside perches so that the birds can enter the pop holes safely. Paint with Cuprinol.

45

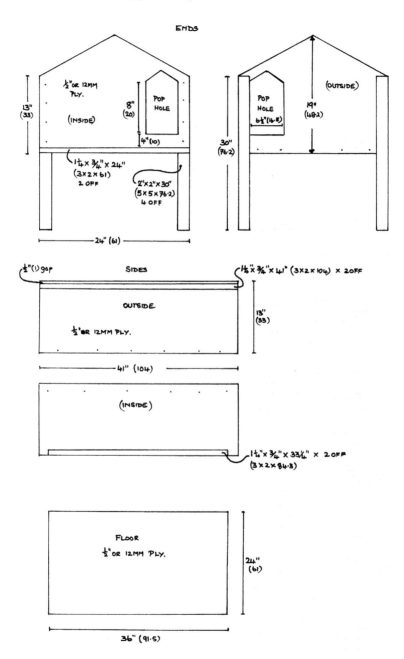

FREE STANDING NEST BOX

ENDS

½" OR 12MM PLY.

(INSIDE)

13" (33)

8" (20)

POP HOLE

4" (10)

1¼" × ¾" × 24" (3 × 2 × 61) 2 OFF

2" × 2" × 30" (5 × 5 × 76·2) 4 OFF

30" (76·2)

24" (61)

POP HOLE
6½" (16·5)

19" (48·2)

(OUTSIDE)

SIDES

½" (1) gap

OUTSIDE

½" OR 12MM PLY.

1¼" × ¾" × 41" (3 × 2 × 104) × 2 OFF

13" (33)

41" (104)

(INSIDE)

1¼" × ¾" × 33¼" × 2 OFF (3 × 2 × 84·3)

FLOOR
½" OR 12MM PLY.

24" (61)

36" (91·5)

46

FREE STANDING NEST BOX

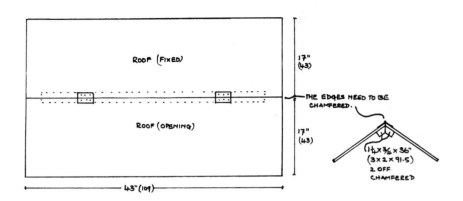

ROOF (FIXED)

17"
(43)

THE EDGES NEED TO BE
CHAMFERED.

ROOF (OPENING)

17"
(43)

1¼ × 3/4 × 36"
(3 × 2 × 91.5)
2 OFF
CHAMFERED

43" (109)

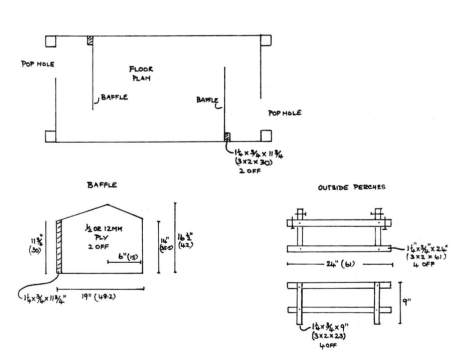

POP HOLE

FLOOR
PLAN

BAFFLE

BAFFLE

POP HOLE

1¼ × 3/4 × 11 3/4
(3 × 2 × 30)
2 OFF

BAFFLE

½ OR 12MM
PLY
2 OFF

11 3/4"
(30)

14"
(350)

16 ½"
(42)

6" (15)

1¼ × 3/4 × 11 3/4"   19" (49.2)

OUTSIDE PERCHES

24" (61)

1¼" × 3/4" × 24"
(3 × 2 × 61)
4 OFF

9"

1¼ × 3/4 × 9"
(3 × 2 × 23)
4 OFF

47

FOLDING SAW BENCH

When one moves into a new property there is always a great deal of clearing up to do, and a saw bench like this is invaluable.

When you look at the drawings, both sides appear the same, the only difference being the top 4" x 1" rail which protrudes 2" on either side. This is to stop the bench from collapsing when opened out.

The bolts should be bored out to 1/2" and countersunk at both ends for the bolt head and the bolt nut. The reason for 'hiding' the bolts is that if you slip while using the chain saw, there isn't a shower of sparks if you hit one of them.

This saw bench folds flat which is useful, as it is rather bulky when extended, but a reasonable weight to lift.

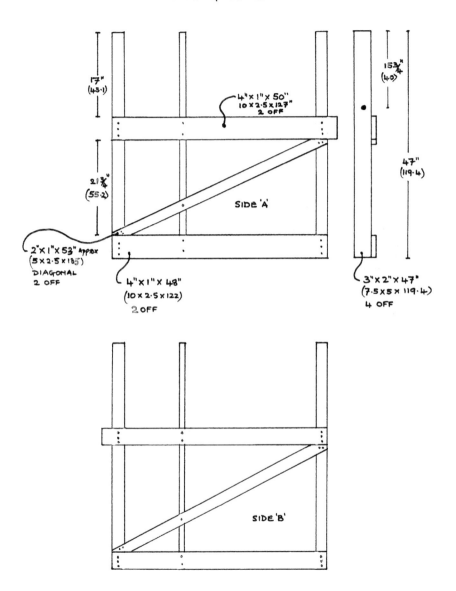

17"
(43·1)

4"x1"x 50"
10 x 2·5 x 127"
2 OFF

21¾"
(55·2)

SIDE 'A'

153¾"
(40)

47"
(119·4)

2"x1"x 53" approx
(5 x 2·5 x 135)
DIAGONAL
2 OFF

4"x1"x 48"
(10 x 2·5 x 122)
2 OFF

3"x2"x47"
(7·5x5x 119·4)
4 OFF

SIDE 'B'

BOLTS: 2 OFF ½"(12MM) 3"(7·5) LONG.
1 OFF ½" (12MM) 1½"(4) LONG
THESE ARE COUNTERSUNK IN.

RAT BOX

I must have made hundreds of these, as it is such a safe way to trap or poison rats, mice and squirrels.

It is best to cut as many as you can out of an 8' x 4' sheet of 3/8" plyboard or sheathing board.

Cut the 6" x 1" board into 6 1/2" lengths; some you use for middle divisions, some you saw in half to make fronts. Cut out the holes in the middle divisions, and then fix the sides to them. The gap between the middle divisions is 6". Fix on the fronts and then the floor. I use panel pins on the ends of the plyboard.

Take the top piece of plyboard and nail on the 1 1/4" x 3/4" lath rails. The top should fit easily, to slide along if necessary.

Give the box a good coat of dark Cuprinol, (several times if you can) and allow it to dry thoroughly.

You will discover how to use this box in Modern Vermin Control, one of the books in our Gold Cockerel Series. Always use with a house brick on the top.

RAT BOX.

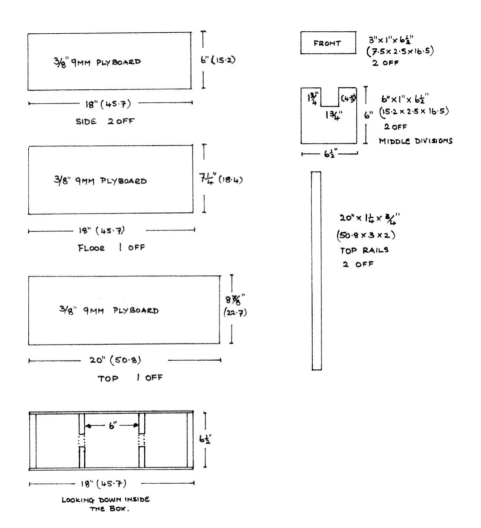

3/8" 9MM PLYBOARD   6" (15·2)

18" (45·7)

SIDE   2 OFF

3/8" 9MM PLYBOARD   7¼" (18·4)

18" (45·7)

FLOOR   1 OFF

3/8" 9MM PLYBOARD   8⅝" (22·7)

20" (50·8)

TOP   1 OFF

6"

6½"

18" (45·7)

LOOKING DOWN INSIDE
THE BOX.

FRONT   3"×1"×6½"
(7·5×2·5×16·5)
2 OFF

1¾"   (4·3)
1¾"   6"   6"×1"×6½"
(15·2×2·5×16·5)
2 OFF
MIDDLE DIVISIONS

6½"

20"×1¼×¾"
(50·8×3×2)
TOP RAILS
2 OFF

52

SACK TIDY

When you are feeding a lot of livestock, particularly in winter and spring, there are always lots of empty paper sacks. If not kept tidy they look unsightly and encourage mice, so here is the solution to this problem. String can be inserted underneath the bags to tie them together. My sack tidy at the moment has 52 sacks inside and it is about 2/3 full.

SCOOP HOLDER

If you are feeding different rations at one time, there is often a few minutes of "hunt the scoop". With this simple holder, which can be placed on a wall near your sacks of food, you always know where the scoop is.

53

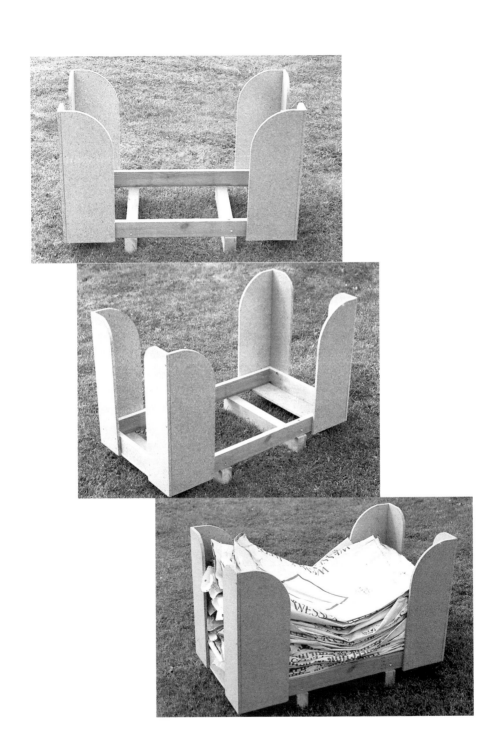

SCOOP HOLDER AND SACK TIDY

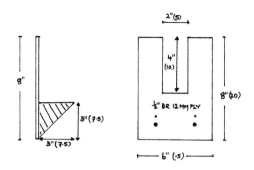

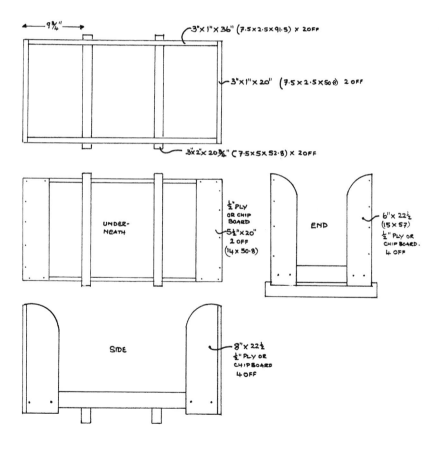

55

GOAT MILKING BENCH

I was asked to produce a milking bench for goats and I came up with this one based on a traditional design having talked to a few goat keepers about milking and their requirements for milking.

This is a mobile milker with wheels (but this facility is optional) which can be taken to the goats rather than the other way round. The ramp at the back slides in and out for transport or for use, and is removable for cleaning. The goat is held by the usual yoke mechanism, and there is provision for a 10" bucket on the front. I have used a rubber car mat (upside down) on the end of the bench which is also removable for cleaning. The bench is quite stable being 18" wide.

Make up the floor bearers and legs first and then fix in the shelf brackets. Screw in the floor boards and attach the side rails. Make up the ramp and fit the sliding rails. Bolt on the handles. Cut out the plyboard for the front section and bucket holder, and assemble. Add the yoke bars and attach the top rails and bore holes for the yoke pins. Next the wheels; turn the bench over, measure the correct height of the centre of your wheels, and drill the legs accordingly. Take care to drill these straight and in line in order to be able to insert the axle correctly.

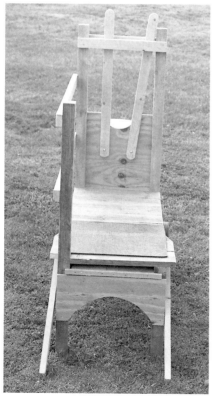

GOAT MILKING BENCH. (SIDES)(FLOOR)

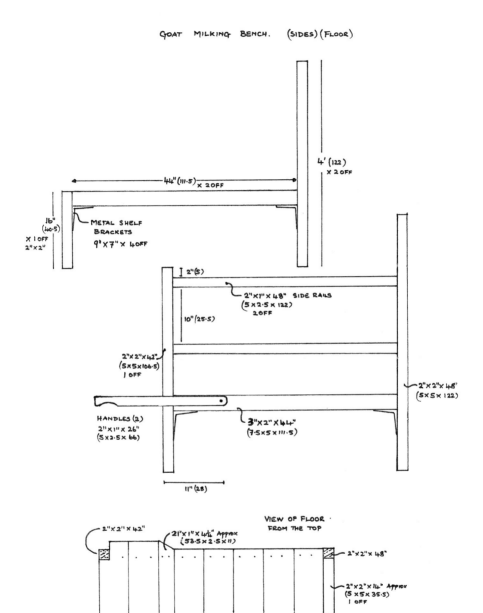

4' (122)
× 2 OFF

44"(111·5) × 2OFF

16"
(40·5)
× 1 OFF
2"×2"

METAL SHELF
BRACKETS
9"×7" × 4 OFF

2"(5)

2"×1"× 48" SIDE RAILS
(5×2·5× 122)
2 OFF

10"(25·5)

2"×2"×42"
(5×5×106·5)
1 OFF

2"×2"× 48'
(5×5× 122)

HANDLES (2)
2"×1"× 26"
(5×2·5× 66)

3"×2"×44"
(7·5×5× 111·5)

11" (28)

VIEW OF FLOOR
FROM THE TOP

2"×2"× 42"

21"×1"× 4½" Approx
(53·5×2·5×11)

2"×2"× 48'

2"×2"×14" Approx
(5 ×5× 35·5)
1 OFF

2"×2"× 48

6"×1"×21"
15×2·5×53·5
× 2 OFF

6"×1"×18" × 5 OFF
15×2·5×45·8)

58

GOAT MILKING BENCH (RAMP, BACK END, FRONT END)

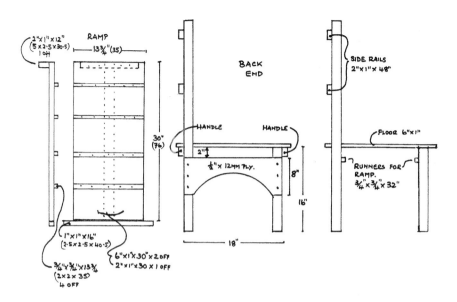

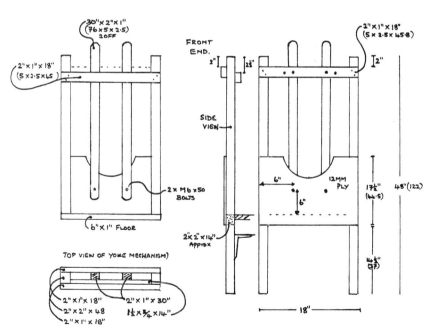

59

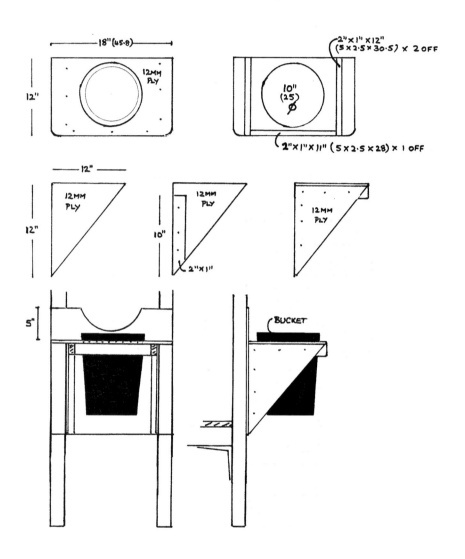

60

MILKING STOOL

I wanted a simple light milking stool, which could be made with limited carpentry skills. Most milking stools are three legged, some have only one leg and the stool is strapped to the milker's bottom, but I wanted to avoid mitred joints and angled legs, so I came up with this simple design. It is very solid and yet light in weight, and it has a central grip hole to hold it by.

Cut the lengths for the top and screw these to the 2" x 1". Then screw the legs to the 2" x 1". Now cut out the plyboard; I used a paint tin as a guide for the arched semi-circle hole and cut it out with a jigsaw. Screw these pieces on, making sure that everything is square and level. Sand paper all round.

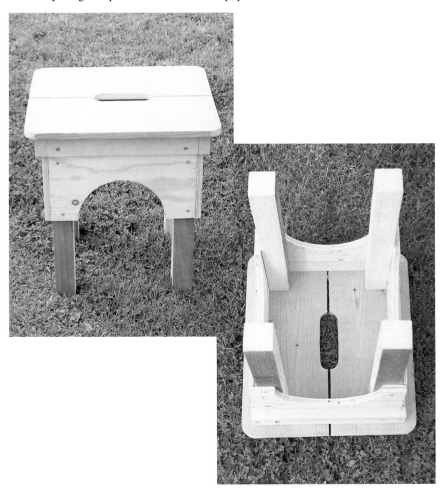

MILKING STOOL

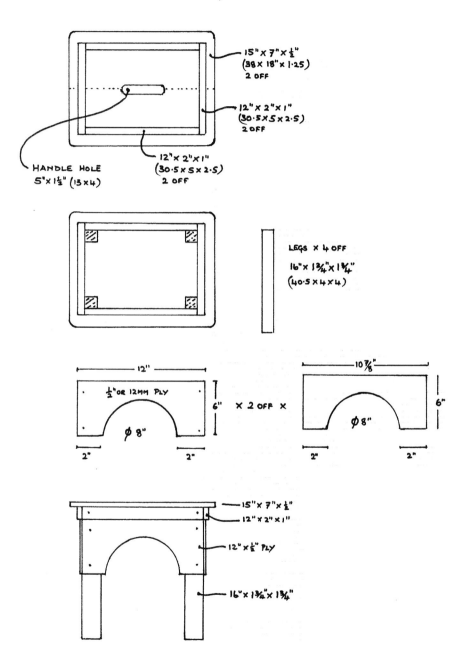

15" × 7" × ½"
(38 × 18" × 1·25)
2 OFF

12" × 2" × 1"
(30·5 × 5 × 2·5)
2 OFF

12" × 2" × 1"
(30·5 × 5 × 2·5)
2 OFF

HANDLE HOLE
5" × 1½" (13 × 4)

LEGS × 4 OFF
16" × 1¾" × 1¾"
(40·5 × 4 × 4)

12"

½" OR 12MM PLY

6"

⌀ 8"

2"   2"

× 2 OFF ×

10⅞"

6"

⌀ 8"

2"   2"

15" × 7" × ½"
12" × 2" × 1"
12" × ½" PLY
16" × 1¾" × 1¾"

GOAT HOUSE

You rarely see housing for goats, and most people keep them in stables or partitioned-off areas in barns. I came up with this design which is easy to make, is on two skids for moving around, and the roof slides either way for access inside. There is a small door at one end which of course could be increased in size to accommodate larger goats, but the design was made mainly so they could clamber on and off the house, which they love to do, particularly the kids. The ventilation is under the roof, and more could be added either end if this was felt necessary.

Cut the skids to length, and the front diagonal. Bore the holes so that a rope or chain can be attached to the skids when you want to move the house around. Build on the 2" x 2" and then add the plyboard floor; this will make the whole construction square. Build up the ends and fix them to the floor. Now make up the sides and fix all round the floor and ends. Cut out the roof pieces and fix on the 3" x 2", then add the 4 battens leaving space for ventilation. Add on the plyboard roof; this should slide easily, and when you want to muck out the house, just half slide it off and clamber inside. The house must be given several coats of Cuprinol in order to preserve the plyboard.

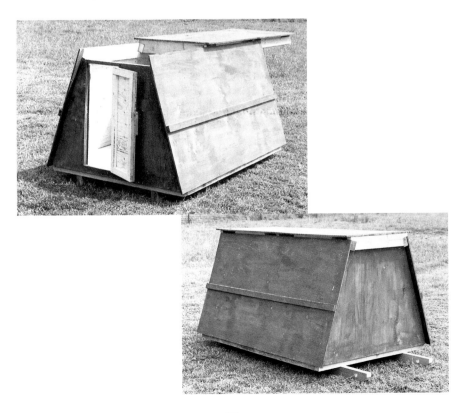

GOAT HOUSE.   FLOOR CONSTRUCTION.

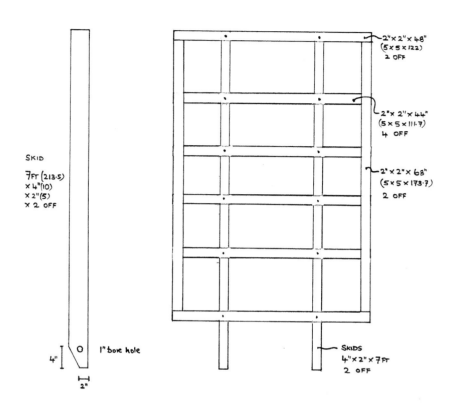

SKID

7FT (213·5)
× 4"(10)
× 2"(5)
× 2 OFF

4"   O   1" bore hole

2"

2"× 2"× 48"
(5×5×122)
2 OFF

2"× 2"× 44"
(5×5×111·7)
4 OFF

2"× 2"× 68"
(5×5×173·7)
2 OFF

SKIDS
4"× 2"× 7FT
2 OFF

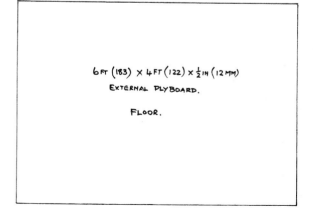

6FT (183) × 4FT (122) × ½IN (12MM)
EXTERNAL PLYBOARD.

FLOOR.

64

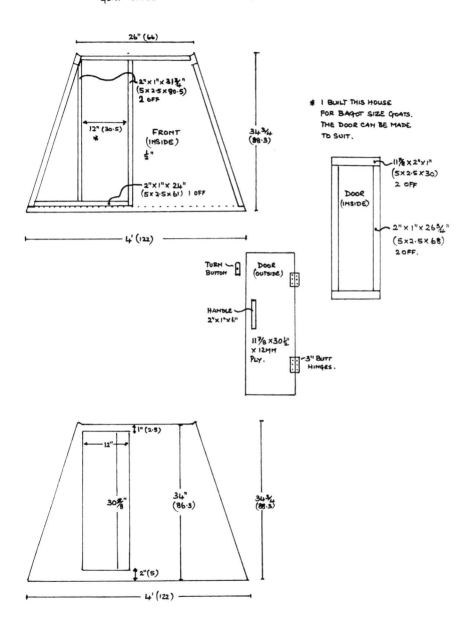

26" (66)

2"x1"x31¾"
(5x2·5x80·5)
2 OFF

12" (30·5)
*

FRONT
(INSIDE)
½"

34¾"
(88·3)

2"x1"x24"
(5x2·5x61) 1 OFF

4' (122)

* I BUILT THIS HOUSE
FOR BAGOT SIZE GOATS.
THE DOOR CAN BE MADE
TO SUIT.

11⅞ X 2"x1"
(5x2·5x30)
2 OFF

DOOR
(INSIDE)

2"x1"x26¾"
(5x2·5x68)
2 OFF.

TURN
BUTTON

DOOR
(OUTSIDE)

HANDLE
2"x1"x6"

11⅞ X 30½"
X 12MM
PLY.

3" BUTT
HINGES.

1" (2·5)

12"

30⅞"

34"
(86·3)

34¾"
(88·3)

2"(5)

4' (122)

65

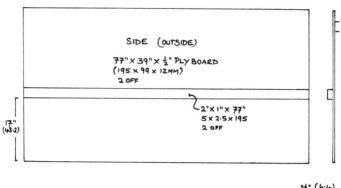

SIDE (OUTSIDE)

77" X 39" X ½" PLY BOARD
(195 × 99 × 12MM)
2 OFF

2"X 1" X 77"
5 × 2.5 × 195
2 OFF

17"
(43.2)

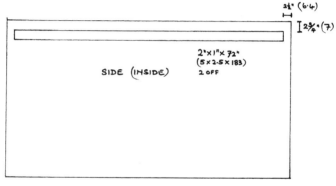

2½" (6.4)

2¾" (7)

2"X 1" X 72"
(5 × 2.5 × 183)
2 OFF

SIDE (INSIDE)

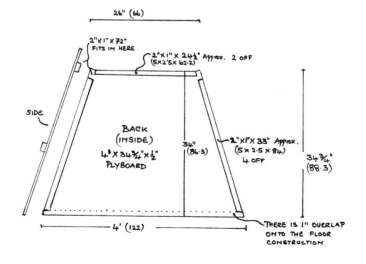

26" (66)

2"X 1" X 72"
FITS IN HERE

2"X 1" X 24½" Approx. 2 OFF
(5×2.5× 62.2)

SIDE

BACK
(INSIDE)
4' X 34¾" X ½"
PLYBOARD

34"
(86.3)

2"X 1"X 33" Approx.
(5 × 2.5 × 84)
4 OFF

34¾"
(88.3)

4' (122)

THERE IS 1" OVERLAP
ONTO THE FLOOR
CONSTRUCTION

GOAT HOUSE ROOF CONSTRUCTION.

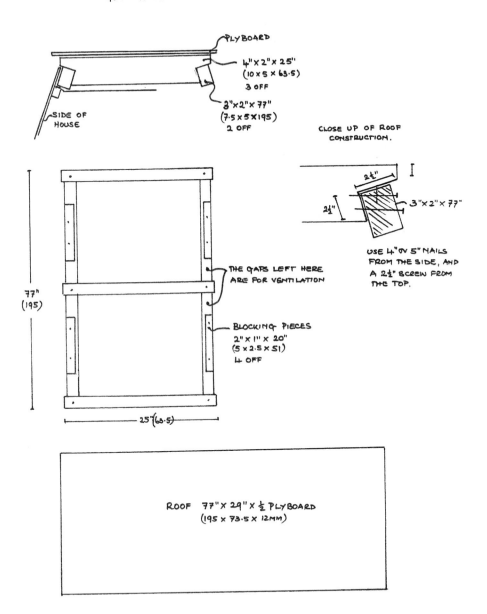

PLYBOARD

4" X 2" X 25"
(10 x 5 x 63.5)
3 OFF

3" X 2" X 77"
(7.5 x 5 X 195)
2 OFF

SIDE OF
HOUSE

CLOSE UP OF ROOF
CONSTRUCTION.

2¼"

2¼"

3" X 2" X 77"

USE 4" OV 5" NAILS
FROM THE SIDE, AND
A 2½" SCREW FROM
THE TOP.

77"
(195)

THE GAPS LEFT HERE
ARE FOR VENTILATION

BLOCKING PIECES
2" X 1" X 20"
(5 x 2.5 x 51)
4 OFF

25" (63.5)

ROOF 77" X 29" X ½ PLYBOARD
(195 x 73.5 x 12mm)

67

POULTRY SECTIONS (6FT OR 10FT)

I have used these for years; they were originally used by game farmers, and still are, to section areas. The great joy of these sections is that you can release your youngstock into a large area 6ft x 6ft or 10ft x 10ft, with netting on top, and know they are safe from hawks, buzzards, crows and magpies. How often you move them depends on the time of year and how wet the ground is; they are very quick and easy to move with two people. The netting I use is tarred 2" x 2" string which the larger game farmers sell. I half hammer in felt nails every 18" along the top rail of the section, and pull the netting semi-taut across. If you pull the netting too taut it will shrink if the sun comes out and dries it, and will often snap the top rail - so beware!

Place the two cut boards on the floor, and nail on the uprights. It is best to use long nails and turn over the ends to give extra strength and to stop the boards from pulling off. Add in the top rail - you may need to drill and nail in order to stop the ends from splitting. Roll the wire netting out, 3ft x 1" or 1/2", whichever you require, staple squarely at one end, and pull tight across the length of the section. Staple along the top rail and then stretch and staple along the top board. I use a staple gun, and then run the hammer over the staples that protrude. I always use tanalised wood for these sections, and providing you put them away in the winter they last for years.

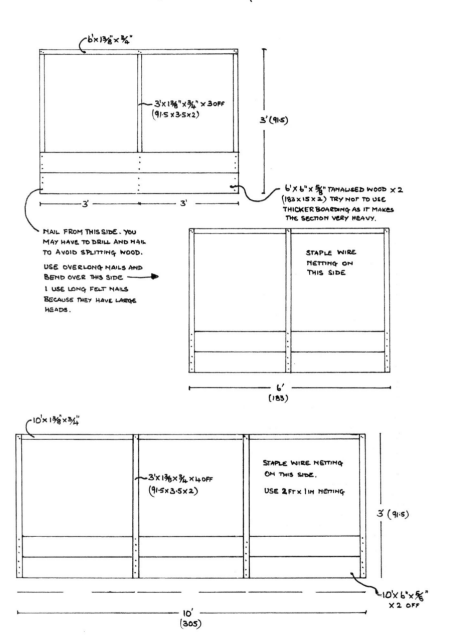

6' x 1⅜" x ¾"

3' x 1⅜" x ¾" x 3 OFF
(91·5 x 3·5 x 2)

3' (91·5)

3'

3'

6' x 6" x ⅝" TANALISED WOOD x 2
(183 x 15 x 2) TRY NOT TO USE
THICKER BOARDING AS IT MAKES
THE SECTION VERY HEAVY.

NAIL FROM THIS SIDE. YOU
MAY HAVE TO DRILL AND NAIL
TO AVOID SPLITTING WOOD.

USE OVERLONG NAILS AND
BEND OVER THIS SIDE ➤
I USE LONG FELT NAILS
BECAUSE THEY HAVE LARGE
HEADS.

STAPLE WIRE
NETTING ON
THIS SIDE

6'
(183)

10' x 1⅜" x ¾"

3' x 1⅜" x ¾" x 4 OFF
(91·5 x 3·5 x 2)

STAPLE WIRE NETTING
ON THIS SIDE.

USE 2 FT x 1 IN NETTING

3' (91·5)

10' x 6" x ⅝"
X 2 OFF

10'
(305)

70

NOTES

NOTES

NOTES

NOTES